STRONG
and TRUE

A Beka Book® Pensacola, FL 32523-9100
an affiliate of PENSACOLA CHRISTIAN COLLEGE®

Strong and True
Third Edition

Staff Credits
Compiling Editor: Laurel Hicks
Illustrator: Walter Kerr
Edition Editor: Catherine Pendley
Cover Design: Michelle Johnson
Cover Illustrator: Jon Seest

Cataloging Data
Hicks, Laurel.
      Strong and true / by Laurel Hicks; illustrated
   by Walter Kerr. — 3rd ed.
   125 p.: col. ill., 23cm. (A Beka Book reading program)
   1. Reading (Primary) 2. Readers (Primary) III. Kerr,
Walter. IV. A Beka Book, Inc.
Library of Congress: PE1119 .H525 2005
Dewey System: 428.4

To the Teacher

Children are eagerly searching for a workable sense of values. They need to see in the lives of great people, common people, and children like themselves, the unchanging values of the ages lived out. They need reading material that will give them ideals to reach for and examples to follow.

The stories in *Strong and True* have been selected from the readers of America's past and have been edited, modernized, and classroom-tested for student appeal and readability. These values are taught throughout the book—honesty, integrity, courage, faith, kindness, forgiveness, industry, unselfishness, patriotism, and respect for authority. Thought questions at the end of the stories greatly aid in the understanding and appreciation of the selections. *Strong and True* should be read after students have mastered Phonics Charts 1–11 and while they are learning Phonics Charts 12–13.

Contents

Stories

Poetry

Words to Watch For

Elsa   Grandma   wrinkles
every   doesn't   sparkle

Little Sunshine

Long ago, there was a little girl named Elsa. She had a very old grandmother with white hair, and wrinkles all over her face.

Elsa's father had a large house that stood on a hill.

Each day the sun peeped in at the south windows. It made everything look bright and shiny.

The grandmother lived on the north side of the house. The sun never came to her room.

One day Elsa said to her father, "Why doesn't the sun peep into Grandma's room? I know she would like to have him."

"The sun cannot look in at the north windows," said her father.

"Then let us turn the house around, Father."

"It is much too large for that," said her father.

"Will Grandma never have any sunshine in her room?" asked Elsa.

"No, my child, unless you can carry some to her."

After that Elsa tried and tried to think how she could carry the sunshine to her grandmother.

When she played in the fields she saw the grass and the flowers nodding their heads. The birds sang sweetly as they flew from tree to tree.

Everything seemed to say, "We love the sun. We love the bright, warm sun."

"Grandma would love it, too," thought the child. "I must take some to her."

When she was in the garden one morning, she felt the sun's warm rays in her golden hair. Then she sat down, and she saw them in her lap.

"I will take them in my dress," she thought, "and carry them to Grandma's room." So she jumped up and ran into the house.

"Look, Grandma, look! I have some sunshine for you," she cried. And she opened her dress, but there was not a ray to be seen.

"It peeps out of your eyes, my child," said her grandmother, "and it shines in your sunny, golden hair. I do not need the sun when I have you with me."

Elsa did not understand how the sun could peep out of her eyes. But she was glad to make her dear grandmother happy.

Every morning she played in the garden. Then she ran to her grandmother's room to carry the sunshine in her eyes and hair.

The dear grandmother told her stories until the little girl's eyes sparkled with joy.

Sunbeams

Kind words are like sunbeams,
That sparkle as they fall;
And loving smiles are sunshine,
A light of joy to all.

The Bible Says

"Let your light so shine before men, that they may see your good works, and glorify your Father which is in Heaven."

—*Matthew 5:16*

The Raven and the Robin

Words to Watch For

warm	only	any	ever
raven	robin	maple	simple

One morning in spring a raven was sitting on one of the branches of an old apple tree.

He looked very cross, and could only say, "Croak, croak."

Soon a little robin came with a song into the same tree. "Good morning to you," she said to the raven.

But the raven would not look at the robin; he looked only at the clouds and croaked something about the cold wind.

"I told you good morning," said the robin.

"You seem very happy this morning," said the raven.

"Why should I not be happy?" asked the robin. "Spring has come, and everybody should be glad and happy."

"I am not happy," said the raven. "Don't you see those black clouds? It is going to snow."

"Very well," said the robin, "I shall go on singing till it comes. A song will not make it any colder."

"You are a very simple bird," said the raven.

Then the robin flew to a maple tree and sang for a long time; but the raven sat still and made himself very unhappy. "The wind is so cold," he said. "It never seems to blow from the right way for me."

Very soon the sun came out warm and bright, and the clouds went away. But the simple raven was as sad as ever.

The grass began to spring up in the fields. Green leaves and flowers were seen in the woods.

Birds flew here and there in the glad sunshine. The raven sat alone on the branch of the old apple tree.

"It is always too warm or too cold," said he. "The sun is shining just now, but it will not be long till it will burn me up. After that, it will be colder than before. I don't see how anyone can be so silly as to sing."

Just then the robin came back with a straw in her mouth. "Well, my friend," asked she, "where is your snow?"

"Don't say anything," croaked the raven; "it will snow all the harder for this sunshine."

"And snow or rain," said the robin, "you will keep on croaking. For my part, I shall look on the bright side of everything, and have a song for every day in the year."

Which was wiser, the raven or the robin?

The Melancholy Pig

There was a Pig that sat alone,
    Beside a ruined pump.
By day and night he made his moan:
    It would have stirred a heart of stone
To see him wring his hoofs and groan
    Because he could not jump.

—Lewis Carroll

Words to Watch For

doesn't   he'll   didn't   we're

Ring and the Bone

"Here, Ring. Here, Ring," called Paul. "Here's a big bone for you. Mother said you could have it."

"Arf!" said Ring as he grabbed the bone. It was his way of saying, "Thank you!"

"Oh, look Paul," said Joy. "Ring likes his bone. See him shake it back and forth in his mouth."

"Now where is he going?" said Paul. "Do you think he'll hide the bone, Joy? Let's follow him and see."

Ring ran this way. Then he ran that way.

"Wait, Ring!" called Joy. "Now you're running too fast for us."

"Now look," said Paul. "Ring is running to the stream. Hurry up, Joy. Let's catch up with him. I want to see what he'll do."

Ring ran faster and faster until he came to the stream.

Ring ran onto the bridge. He ran right to the middle of the bridge, and then he stopped.

"What is he doing now?" said Paul. "What is he looking at in the water?"

"I know," said Joy. "Ring thinks he sees another dog in the water. The other dog has a bone, too."

"But that's not a dog," said Paul. "Ring just sees his own face."

"I know," said Joy. "But Ring doesn't know that. Listen to him growl."

Ring growled and growled at the dog in the water.

"Ring wants that dog's bone," said Joy. "Shame on you, Ring. You have one bone already. Don't be so greedy.

But Ring did not listen to Joy. He kept on growling. "Gr-r-r," he said. "Gr-r-r-ruf!"

Still the dog in the water just looked at Ring. Ring growled louder and louder. Then he jumped.

But Ring did not find the dog. He did not find the bone. All he found was a cold, wet stream. Down his bone went to the bottom of the stream.

"Oh, Ring," said Paul. "You were too greedy. You didn't get the other bone, and now you lost your own bone, too."

Ring came out of the water. Then he began to shake. He shook, and he shook, and he shook.

"Stop, Ring!" cried Joy. "Now we're wet, too. You're a bad, bad dog!"

"Come on, Joy," said Paul. "Let's take Ring home and get him dry. After all, he's just a dog. Dogs don't know that it's wrong to be greedy."

And Paul and Joy and Ring went home to dry off.

What Do You Think?

1. Was Ring happy when Paul gave him a bone?
2. Was Ring happy when he saw the dog in the water?
3. Was Ring as smart as Joy and Paul? How do you know?
4. Did Ring know that it is wrong to be greedy?
5. How are you different from Ring?
6. What things has God given you that you can be happy with?

The Bible Says

". . . Be content with such things as ye have: for He hath said, I will never leave thee, nor forsake thee."
—*Hebrews 13:5*

God's Care

Do you know how many stars
Are shining in the sky?
Do you know how many clouds
Each day go floating by?
God, the Lord, has counted all;
He would miss one, should it fall.

Do you know how many children
Go to bed at night,
That, without a care or trouble,
Wake up with the morning light?
God, in Heaven, each name can tell.
He knows you too, and loves you well.

Words to Watch For

country   someone   enter

through   tearing   anyone

ago   together   quietly

Why the Deer Has Antlers

Long, long ago, the deer had no antlers.

He was a great runner. All the animals knew it.

The rabbit was a great jumper. The animals knew this, too. They had seen him going over the ground very fast.

"I wonder if he can jump faster than the deer can run," said one animal.

That started them talking, and they talked and talked. Some thought the deer could run faster. Some thought the rabbit could jump faster. After much talk, they planned a race.

A fine large pair of antlers was to be the prize.

It was planned for them to run through the woods and back again. There were many bushes in the woods.

It would be hard work to run through such bushy woods.

The plan was to have them start together. The one who came back first would get the antlers.

On the day of the race, all the animals came to the starting place. The antlers were put down on the ground to show the starting place.

Everyone was looking at the antlers, thinking and saying what fine horns they were. The rabbit was doing some thinking, too.

"This is new country to me," he said. "I want to take a look through the bushes where I am to run."

The other animals thought this was fair. So off he went.

But he stayed and he stayed. It was long past time for the race to begin. The animals began to look at each other.

"I think we should send someone to find him," said Mr. Squirrel. He knew that the rabbit was full of tricks.

They sent Mr. Fox off to find him. What do you suppose he saw?

He saw the rabbit in the middle of the woods, tearing away at the bushes, biting them off and pulling them away. He was making himself a nice little path through the woods.

The fox turned around quietly and came back. He told the other animals what he had seen. There were some who didn't believe it.

By and by the rabbit came, hop-hop-hop.

"Am I late?" he asked.

Then they told him what the fox had said. Do you know he stood there and said it was not so? He jumped up and down and said the fox had not seen him.

At that the animals all went to see. There they saw for themselves the nice little path.

The animals decided there would be no race. Anyone who played tricks like that had no right to enter a race at all. They handed the antlers to the deer. He put them on and has worn them ever since.

They told the rabbit that from that day on, he would have to cut down bushes for a living. And to this day he does.

What Do You Think?

1. Is this a true story? How do you know?
2. Who really gave the deer his horns? How do you know?
3. If the other animals had not discovered the rabbit's trick, the rabbit might have won the race. Do you think that winning a race in that way would have made the rabbit happy? Why not?

country	enough	merchant
honest	young	trouble
own	owner	buy

A **merchant** is a person who buys and sells things.

Honest means always telling the truth.

Two Honest Men

In a far-away country there once lived a poor man who had long wanted to have a home that he could call his own. He worked very hard, and at last saved enough money to buy a little farm.

One day as he was plowing in one of his fields, he turned up a pot that was full of gold.

"Oh, how rich I would be if this gold were only my own!" he said.

Nobody saw him when he found the gold, and he might have kept it all for himself if he had wished. "But no," he said. "It is not mine. I may never be rich, but I can always be honest."

He had paid a good price for his farm, but he did not think that he had bought the gold that was in the ground.

He took up the gold, and carried it to the merchant who had sold him the land. He said to him, "Here is some gold that was left in the ground I bought from you. I turned it up with my plow this morning."

"Why do you bring it to me?" said the merchant.

"Because it belongs to you," said the farmer.

"No, it does not. It belongs to you, for I sold you the field and all that was in it. The gold is not mine, and I shall not take any of it."

But the farmer said, "I paid for nothing but the land. The gold is not mine, but yours."

For a long time the two men talked, each trying to make the other take the gold. Both were honest, and neither would keep what he thought did not belong to him.

Their friends came around them and said, "Let the farmer keep half, and the merchant half." But they did not think it was right to do even this.

At last the farmer said, "Let us go and tell the king about it. He will know what is best."

"Yes," said the merchant. "Let us go and tell him."

The king heard first the farmer and then the merchant. "It is hard to tell which of you is owner of the gold," he said. "But it is easy to see that you are both very honest men."

Then he asked if they had any children. "I have a son," said the

merchant. "And I have a daughter," said the farmer.

"Then," said the king, "I can tell you what to do with the gold. If the merchant's son will marry the farmer's daughter, it can be given to the young people, and they can buy themselves a home with it."

Nothing could have pleased the merchant's son more than this, and the farmer's daughter was well pleased, too, for the young man was good-looking and brave. And so the trouble was soon ended, and everybody was made glad.

That year there was more corn in the farmer's fields than had ever grown before, and the merchant sold so many goods that he had all the gold he could use.

The Bible Says

"Speak ye every man the truth to his neighbor."
—Zechariah 8:16

The Selfish Dog in the Manger

Words to Watch For

manger	finally	course	most
anyone	snarling	snapped	blankets

There was once a cross little dog who lay all day long panting and snarling in a manger, where there was some good hay.

A big goat came into the barn for his dinner. "Please get out of the manger," he said to the dog. "I want to eat some hay for my dinner."

"I will not get out," snapped the dog.

Feeling very hungry, the goat left the barn.

The old sheep came into the barn next. "Please move over a bit," she said politely to the dog. "I would like to eat my dinner now."

"Move over yourself," snarled the dog.

Feeling both hungry and hurt, the sheep left the barn.

Finally a big farm horse came into the barn and looked at the hay.

The dog did not even give the horse a chance to speak. He began to growl and bark and snap at the horse with his teeth. "Go away at once," he said to the horse. "I am tired of all these animals who try to disturb my hay."

"Are you planning to eat the hay?" asked the horse.

"Of course not," snarled the dog. "Anyone knows that dogs don't eat hay."

"Then please let me eat it," cried the horse. "I have been working hard all day pulling a wagon, and I am very hungry. If you just want to lie down, why don't you lie on those soft blankets over in the corner?"

"No," snapped the dog. "I am in the manger, and in the manger I will stay. No one can make me move if I don't want to. You go away or I will chew your ear off."

"What a mean, selfish dog you are," said the old horse sadly. "You can't eat the hay, and yet you won't let anyone else have it. You are the most selfish animal in the whole barnyard."

Feeling hungry, hurt, and sad, the horse went away.

And the animals of the barnyard never went near that selfish dog again.

What Do You Think?

1. What do you think of the dog in the manger?
2. Do you think that he had any friends? Why not?

The Bible Says

"As ye would that men should do to you, do ye also to them likewise." —*Luke 6:31*

The Way to Be Happy

Words to Watch For

servants   clothes   busy   whose
trouble   envy   owe

Envy means wanting something that belongs to someone else.

A very long time ago, there was a king whose name was Henry.

He lived in a fine house and he had many servants to wait upon him. He had fine clothes, beautiful horses, strong boxes full of gold, and many ships that sailed upon the sea.

He had everything that anyone could wish for. And yet he was not happy.

In the same country there was a poor miller who had a little mill close by the river Dee.

This miller was busy every hour of the day, and he was as happy as he was busy. People who lived near the mill heard him singing all the time from morning till night.

When anyone asked why he was so happy, he said, "I have all that I need, and I do not wish for more."

One day the king was in great trouble. "Tell me," he said, "if there is one happy man in all this land."

His friends said, "We have heard that there is one such man. He is a miller, and he lives by the river Dee."

"I must see this miller of the Dee," said the king. "I will learn from him how to be happy."

The very next day King Henry rode down to the river Dee. He stopped his horse at the door of the little mill. He could hear the miller singing at his work:

"I envy nobody; no, not I,
And nobody envies me."

The king went into the mill. He said to the miller, "You are wrong, my

friend; for I envy you. I would give all that I have if I could be as happy as you."

The miller said, "I will help you to be happy if I can."

"Then tell me," said the king, "why it is that you can sing this song in your little mill on the Dee, while I, who am king of all the land, am sad every day of my life?"

The miller smiled and said, "This is why I am happy in my little mill: I trust in God each day. I work, and earn my food. I love my wife and children, and I love my friends. I owe no man, and the good river Dee turns the mill that grinds the corn to feed my family and me."

The king turned sadly away. "Goodby, my friend," he said. "Be happy while you may. I would rather be the miller of the Dee than king of all this land."

"So would I," said the happy miller.

Why was the miller happy? It was because he trusted in God, he had good friends, he owed no man, and he did not wish for things which he could not have.

Why was the king not happy? He knew that men did not love him, and he was never content with what he had. He did not have God's love in his heart. Do you think he would have been happy if the miller had given him his mill? Why not?

Think of This!

The world is so full of a
number of things,
I'm sure we should all be as
happy as kings.

—*Robert Louis Stevenson*

The Bible Says

"Happy is that people, whose God is the Lord." —*Psalm 144:15*

general soldiers bothering distress

General Robert E. Lee was a great soldier.

Distress means being worried and unhappy.

Lee and the Bird

One day General Robert E. Lee was on a battlefield. The big guns were booming all around.

His men said, "You must not stay here, General Lee. You may be killed. What would we do without our leader? Go away, go away!"

General Lee turned to go. Suddenly he stopped and looked down.

A mother bird was flying around. She flew to the ground. Then she flew to a tree near General Lee, and then she flew back again to the same place on the ground.

All the time she was calling and calling, "Chee, chee! Chee, chee!"

General Lee looked up in the tree. He saw a little nest. Then he looked down on the ground. There lay a little baby bird.

Now he knew what was bothering the mother bird. The little one had fallen out of the nest in the tree. It was too

young to fly back. It lay there on the
ground and called to its mother.

The poor little mother could not take
it back to the nest. She would not
leave it, so she stayed there among the
soldiers, with the big guns booming all
around her. She kept on flying from
the nest to the baby bird, from the bird
to the nest, calling and calling in distress, "Chee, chee, chee!"

Again the men said to their general,
"You must go, General Lee. We will not
fight until you are safe."

But the great general would not leave
that mother bird in distress. He
stooped down and picked up the baby
bird. He put it back into its nest, and
saw the little mother fly to it.

Then he went away.

What Do You Think?

1. What do you think of Robert E. Lee?
2. Do you think that he was kind to people as
   well as to birds?

Kind Words

Kind hearts are the gardens,
  Kind thoughts are the roots,
Kind words are the flowers,
  Kind deeds are the fruits.

Take care of the gardens,
  And keep them from weeds.
Fill, fill them with flowers,
  Kind words and kind deeds.

—*Henry W. Longfellow*

Words to Watch For

Eyvind   Marit

touched   stretched

Eyvind's Goat

Eyvind had no toys and no one to play with him, but he had one pet that he loved dearly. It was a little goat.

Eyvind kept the goat in a safe place where the fox could not get it. He pulled grass and leaves for it to eat.

One day the goat ran away. It was gone when Eyvind came out to feed it. He thought at once of the fox. Suppose it had caught his dear little goat!

He ran about, looking for his pet and calling, "Goatie! Goatie!"

"Baa!" said the goat at last.

There it was on the hill, looking down at Eyvind. There beside the goat was a little girl.

"Is this your goat?" she asked.

Eyvind opened his mouth and eyes and looked at her.

"Who are you?" he asked.

"I am Marit," she answered. "I am Mother's baby. I am Father's mouse. I am little fairy in Grandfather's house."

Eyvind stood still and looked at the little girl.

"Is this your goat?" she asked again.

"Yes," said Eyvind.

"I like this little goat so much. Will you give it to me?" she asked.

"No, no! I like it, too. I can't give away my little goat."

Marit put her arms around the goat. She looked at Eyvind and said, "If I give you a good cake, may I have the goat?"

Eyvind was very poor. They did not have good things to eat at his home. The only time he had ever tasted cake was once when his grandfather came to see them. He looked up at Marit.

"Let me see the cake," he said.

"Here it is!" she said, and threw it down to Eyvind.

"Oh, it is broken!" said Eyvind.

He picked up every piece of it and then he tasted one little piece. It was so good that he tasted another little piece. Before he thought what he was doing, he had eaten all the cake.

"Now the goat belongs to me," said Marit.

"Oh, no! You can't have my little goat," said Eyvind.

Marit laughed and jumped up.

"Yes, yes! The goat is mine," she said. "I said I would give you my cake for the goat. You have eaten the cake. Now the goat is mine, mine, mine!"

Marit put a strong arm around the goat's neck and tried to lead it away. At first it would not go with her. It stretched its neck down to Eyvind. "Baa-a-a!" it said.

Marit caught hold of its hair with one hand and pulled at the string with the other hand.

"Come, goatie dear," she said, "you shall stay in the house and eat out of mother's nice dish."

Then she ran away with the goat.

Eyvind was left alone. Oh, how unhappy he was! He loved his little goat so dearly. It was the only little friend he had ever had to play with. Now he had lost it.

His mother had been out at work. On her way home she saw Eyvind. He was sitting at the foot of the hill, crying.

"Eyvind! Eyvind!" she said. "Why are you crying?"

"Oh, my goat! my goat! my little goat!" he cried.

"Where is the goat?" asked his mother, looking around.

"It has gone. It will never come back," said Eyvind.

"What has happened?" she asked. "Where is the little goat?"

"Oh, I sold it. I sold it for a cake!"

"Eyvind! How could you do that?" asked his mother. "Sold your goat for a cake! Oh, what do you suppose the little goat thinks of you?"

Now Eyvind saw how wrong and foolish he had been. He was sure that he never could be happy again as long as he lived.

He cried himself to sleep, and dreamed he saw his little goat. It was far off where he could not get it.

Just as he was dreaming this, something touched him on the ear and waked him. He started up and looked around. There was the goat!

"Oh, you've come back! You've come back," said Eyvind.

He jumped up and took hold of the goat's front legs and danced for joy. He was just going to take the goat home when someone called him. He turned and looked. There was Marit.

Then Eyvind was sad again. "Oh, it is her goat now, not mine," he said to himself.

He stood still and looked at Marit. At last he said, "Have you come back here for your goat?"

Marit said, "It is not my goat. It is yours. Grandfather says it is not right for me to keep it."

"You may play with it," said Eyvind. "Will you play with Goatie and me?"

So Marit and Eyvind played together and became good friends.

What Do You Think?

1. Do you think that Marit was a spoiled little girl? Why do you think so?
2. Why didn't Eyvind want to give his goat away?
3. Do you think that Eyvind planned to eat the cake? What happened?

Words to Watch For

sorry   finger   whole   lose

ripened   thousands watered gathered

The Raindrops

There was once a farmer who had a large field. He had spent much time plowing his field and planting it with corn.

As the little corn plants began to grow, he worked each day to keep the weeds out. The farmer was depending on that corn to provide food and money for his family.

But something was wrong. It had not rained for weeks, and the little corn plants were beginning to dry up and turn brown. The farmer knew that he would lose his whole crop if rain did not come soon, but there was nothing that he could do to bring the rain.

One day, as he stood looking at the blue sky and wishing for rain, two little raindrops, up in the clouds over his head, saw him.

"Look at that farmer," said one. "I feel sorry for him. He has worked so hard in his field, and now his corn is all drying up. I wish I could do him some good."

"Yes," said the other, "but you are only a little raindrop. What can you do? Why, you could not even wet one cornstalk!"

"Well," said the first, "I know that I am too small to do much, but at least I can cheer the farmer up a little. And

I do want to always do my best. The least that I can do is try. I'm going to go down to the field. Good-by!"

Down went the first drop of rain, and the second drop decided to follow. One came splashing on the farmer's nose; the other fell on a stalk of corn.

"Dear me," said the farmer, putting his finger to his nose. "What is that? A raindrop! I do believe it's going to rain."

The first two raindrops had no sooner started for the field, than a third said, "Well if they're going, I think I will, too. Here I come!" And down came that raindrop on another stalk of corn.

By this time, thousands of raindrops had gathered together to hear what their friends were talking about.

When they saw that the first three had gone to help and cheer the farmer,

another drop said, "I want to help, too."
And down he came.

"Me, too! Me, too!" the others cried,
and soon it was raining hard, and the
corn was watered. It now grew and
ripened, all because the first little raindrop had decided to do its best and be
a help.

For he who always does his best,
   His best will better grow,
But he who shirks or slights his task,
   He lets the better go.

The First Thanksgiving

Words to Watch For

England Indians berries squashes

Long ago, the Pilgrims lived in England. They loved God, and they loved the Bible. They wanted to do what is right.

The King of England said, "Everybody must go to my church."

The Pilgrims did not think that God wanted them to go to the king's church. "We must obey God," they said.

The Pilgrims would not go to the king's church. They had their own church. They preached to the people. They told the people that Jesus died for them.

The king became angry and put some of the Pilgrims into prison.

Finally the Pilgrims said, "We must find a new country. We must find a good land where we may worship God in the right way. We must find a land that is free."

The Pilgrims went here and there, but they did not find a land that was free.

At last someone said, "Let's go to America. America is a beautiful, new country. In America we can worship God in the Bible way."

And so the Pilgrims went to America. They sailed for months on their little ship, the <u>Mayflower</u>. Finally they arrived in the beautiful new country.

America was covered with woods in those days. The woods were full of Indians and wild animals.

It was winter when the Pilgrims came. They had cut down trees to build houses. But they could not make the houses warm enough to keep out the cold and the snow.

They had very little food. Many of the Pilgrims became sick, and many died.

Still they trusted God. They said, "God will help us." And God did.

Spring came, and some good Indians came to see the Pilgrims. The Indians showed the Pilgrim children where to find good wild berries.

The Indian fathers showed the Pilgrim fathers the best places to catch fish. The Pilgrims had plenty of food that summer.

Then it was autumn. The corn was tall and ripe. Pumpkins and squashes were growing. The Pilgrim fathers found wild turkeys in the woods.

The happy Pilgrims said, "Let's have a big feast. Let us give thanks to God for our food. Let us thank Him for America, our beautiful new country."

"And let's invite the Indians," the Pilgrims said. "We can share our food with them."

The thankful Pilgrims worked for days to get the feast ready. Then the big day came.

For three days, the Pilgrims and the Indians feasted and played games. But most of all, they thanked God for His wonderful goodness to them.

And that was our first Thanksgiving.

More about the Pilgrims

Why did the Pilgrims come to America?

They came so they could worship God in the way that they felt was right. They came so they could tell people that they needed Jesus in their hearts.

They came so they could preach God's Word without being put into prison. They came to start a new country in which people would be free to do what is right.

What did the Pilgrims bring to America?

The Pilgrims brought God to America. They loved God, and they had God in their hearts. More than anything else, they wanted to serve Him.

The Pilgrims brought the Bible to America, too. They did not just carry their Bibles around with them. They read the Bible, and they believed it.

They started our country on the teachings of the Bible. They believed that God's Word is the most important book in the world.

The Pilgrims also brought themselves to America. They brought their whole selves. They loved the new country they were starting, and they put their whole lives into making it a good country.

They did not just work for their country when they felt like it. They kept right on working, even when hard times came. They loved our country so much that some of them even died for it.

The Pilgrims were not perfect men. They sometimes did wrong and made mistakes just as we do. But they were men who believed God. They were men who obeyed the Bible. They were men who always did their best to make our country great.

The Milkmaid

Words to Watch For

gallons   buy   enough   hatched

Once upon a time a girl was walking along with a pail of milk. She sang a happy song, for she was thinking of the money she would get when she sold her milk. Then she said to herself:

"I have two gallons of milk, which I shall sell. With the money I shall buy fifty eggs. I shall put these under some of my hens. The hens will keep them warm until little chickens are hatched."

"I shall give these chickens plenty of good food and clean water. They will grow fat, and by Christmas they will be large enough to sell. I can get enough money for them to buy a fine new dress."

She was thinking so much about her new dress that she forgot to be careful. Her foot struck a stone. As she tried to keep from falling, the pail flew out of her hands, and the milk was spilled.

Do You Know?

1. Did the milkmaid get all the things she dreamed of having? Why not?
2. When are the best times to dream: When you have work to do? When you are asleep? When you need to listen? When you are alone and not busy?
3. What is the best way to get the things that you want?

The Bible Says

"Whatsoever thy hand findeth to do, do it with thy might."   —*Ecclesiastes 9:10*

The Frog and the Ox

Words to Watch For

pretend   deceive   hoofs   divided

Once a little Frog sat by a big Frog at the side of a pool.

"Oh, Father," said he, "I have just seen the biggest animal in the world.

It was as big as a mountain. It had horns on its head, and it had hoofs divided in two."

"Pooh, child," said the old Frog, "that was only Farmer White's Ox. He is not so very big. I could easily make myself as big as he." And he blew, and he blew, and he blew, and swelled himself out.

"Was he as big as that?" he asked the little Frog.

"Oh, much bigger," said the little Frog.

The old Frog blew, and blew, and blew again, and swelled himself out more than ever.

"Was he bigger than that?" he said.

"Much, much bigger," said the little Frog.

"I can make myself as big," said the old Frog. And once more he blew, and blew, and blew, and swelled himself out,—and he burst!

The little Frog sadly told himself, "I must learn a lesson from this. I must never try to pretend that I am bigger than I am."

The Bible Says

"For if a man think himself to be something, when he is nothing, he deceiveth himself."

—*Galatians 6:3*

wolf   liar   truth   pasture

The Boy Who Cried "Wolf"

Once a little boy was sent by his father to take care of a large flock of sheep.

His father said to him, "If a wolf should come to the pasture, you must call 'Wolf! wolf!' Then the men who are working nearby will come and drive him away."

For many days no wolf came near the flock of sheep. One day the little boy thought he would have some fun with the men. So he cried out, "Wolf! wolf!"

"Where, where?" said the men; and they ran as fast as they could to the pasture.

The little boy said, "There is no wolf; I only wanted to give you a big scare."

The men did not like the boy's fun and went back to their work. Two or three times after that the little boy called the men to drive away the wolf. Each time the men ran to the pasture, but the boy said, "I only wanted to have some fun with you."

At last, a wolf did come to the pasture, and then the little boy shouted, "Help! help! a wolf! a wolf!"

This time the men did not run and help him, for they said, "He only wants to have some fun with us. We will keep right on with our work."

The wolf killed many of the sheep and took one to his den.

When the boy's father found out what had happened, he was very upset. "My son," he said, "you must learn that there is no believing a liar, even when he tells the truth."

The Bible Says

"A false witness shall not be unpunished, and he that speaketh lies shall not escape."

—*Proverbs 19:5*

Be True!

Listen, my boy, I've a word for you;
And this is the word: Be true! be true!
At work or at play, in darkness or light,
Be true, be true, and stand for the
    right.

And you, little girl, I've a word for you;
'Tis the very same: Be true! be true!
For truth is the sun, and falsehood the
    night.
Be true, little maid, and stand for the
    right.

music   sword   Philistines   Goliath

A **shepherd** is a person who takes care of sheep.

David, the Shepherd Boy

David was a shepherd boy. Every day he went to the fields to take care of his father's sheep.

Out in the fields he played on his harp. He made sweet songs to sing to its music.

But he never forgot to tend his sheep.

One day a lion came into the field. It caught a little lamb and ran off with it.

David ran after the lion. He killed the lion and saved the lamb.

Another day a bear came into the field. It caught a little lamb and ran off with it.

David killed the bear and saved this little lamb, too.

Now when David was older, there was a war in the land. David's three oldest brothers went out to fight with Saul, their king. But David stayed at home to tend his father's sheep.

One day David's father said to him, "Take these ten loaves to your brothers in the army, and see how they are."

David rose early in the morning and went to see his brothers in the army.

Saul's army was on one side of a little brook. The army of the Philistines was on the other side of the brook.

Now, there was in the army of the Philistines a great giant named Goliath.

Goliath was more than ten feet tall. He wore a coat of brass. He carried a great sword and a great spear.

The giant Goliath came out in front of the Philistine army and called across the brook to Saul's army.

He said, "Choose a man from your army. Let him come and fight me. If he kills me, all the men in this army will be your servants. If I kill him, you shall be our servants."

The men in Saul's army were afraid of the giant. Not one of them would go out to fight him.

Then David said to King Saul, "I will fight Goliath."

Saul said, "You cannot fight this giant. You are only a boy."

Then David told Saul how he had killed the lion and the bear that came to carry away his lambs. He said, "I am not afraid of the giant. God, Who saved me from the lion and the bear, will save me from Goliath."

Saul saw that David was strong and brave. So he said, "Go, and the Lord be with you."

David took his sling in his hand and went where the Philistines were.

When he came to the brook, he picked up five little stones and put them into his shepherd's bag.

Goliath saw David coming and went out to meet him. When he came near he called, "Come to me and I will give you to be eaten by the birds of the air and the beasts of the field."

David said, "You come to me with a sword and a spear. But I come to you in the name of the Lord. The Lord will give you into my hands."

David ran to meet Goliath. As he ran, he put a stone into his sling. He let the stone fly, and it struck Goliath on the head.

David ran to him and killed him with his own sword. When the Philistines saw Goliath was killed, they ran away. So the shepherd boy saved his people from the Philistines.

When David was a man, he became king.

King David often thought of the days when he was a shepherd boy. He remembered how he had led his sheep to places where there was grass for them to eat. He remembered how he had led them to places where there was water for them to drink.

He thought, "God has cared for me all my life, just as I cared for my sheep." So he took his harp and played and sang a beautiful shepherd song. It is the best-loved shepherd song in the world.

"The Lord is my shepherd;
I shall not want.
He maketh me to lie down in
    green pastures:
He leadeth me beside the still
    waters."

Words to Watch For

probably   different   skeleton
strength   pounce   enemy
protection   spreads

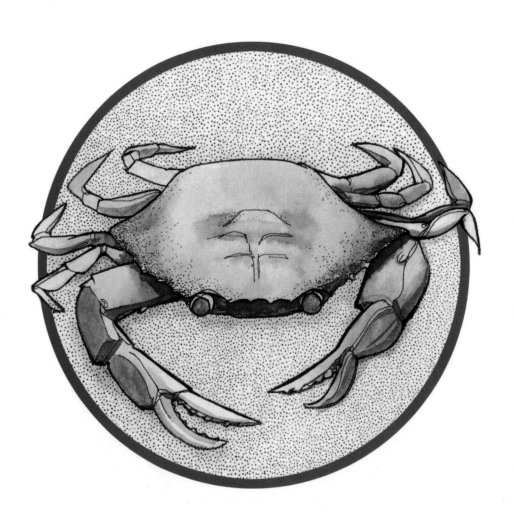

All about Crabs

Have you ever seen a crab? If you live near a beach you probably have seen one. Maybe you have felt one, too!

Crabs are different from people in many ways. You have bones inside your body.

Your bones make a skeleton to hold up your soft flesh.

A crab does not have a skeleton on the inside. His skeleton is on the outside. It is called a shell.

A crab's hard shell protects him from things that would hurt him. Do you know Who gave the crab a hard shell for protection?

A crab has eight legs and two hands. The hands are called pinchers. Can you guess why? When a crab walks, he moves sideways rather than straight ahead.

Crabs use their hands to get food and to dig out homes in the sand. Sometimes they use them to fight, too.

Crabs have eyes set on pegs, or stalks. A crab can push out his eye-pegs and pull them in. How would you look if you could make your eyes stand out six inches from your head?

When the tide is low and there is no water on the beach, Mr. Crab digs out his house. He scoops out the sand with his big claw. Then he folds his claw to carry the sand, the way you would carry grass or leaves on your arm.

Mr. Crab takes the sand to the top of his hole. Then, with a jerk, he throws the sand into a heap.

The crab needs to be very strong for his job of digging. He can lift and carry things larger than his body. Do you know Who planned to give the crab extra strength for a hard job?

Mr. Crab digs out a long hallway. Then he makes rooms for the house.

When the house is done, he and his wife go off to look for food. Crabs like to eat flies, gnats, ants, ladybugs, and other little insects. They also eat sea-weed.

When beach-flies light on the sand or on seaweed, the crabs pounce on them and catch them just as cats catch mice.

Mr. and Mrs. Crab put the bugs they catch into the kitchen of their house.

For six hours each day, while the house is covered with water, the crabs stay inside and eat. They seem to know when the water covers their house. They know when the water moves away and it is safe for them to go outside. Do you know Who taught them these things?

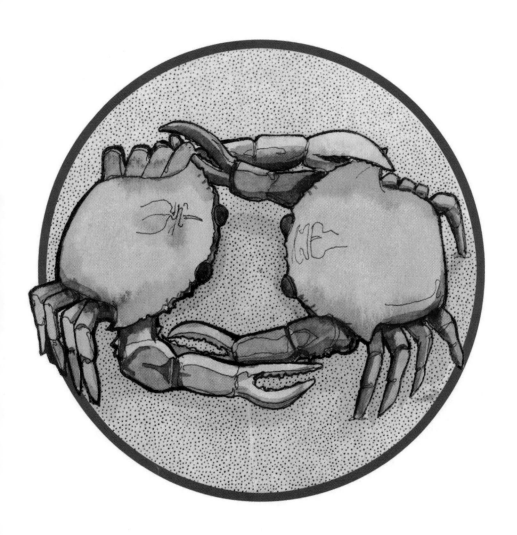

Mr. Crab is quick to get cross. When he sees another crab near his house, he becomes angry. He stands on tiptoes and pulls in his eye-pegs so they will not get hurt. He spreads out his big arm. Now he is ready to fight!

He runs at his enemy. Each tries to hit the other with his big claw, which can cut and pinch hard.

Sometimes one crab cuts off the hand or leg of the other crab, or bites the shell on his back.

If only a leg is cut off, the crab may keep on fighting. But if his hand, or eye, or back shell is hurt, he runs home to hide.

And then do you know what he does? He grows a new eye or hand or leg! Could you do that?

I guess God knew that crabs would be fighters, but He never planned for people to act like crabs!

Words to Watch For

Persia   common   uncommon

poured   business   Hassan

Filling a Basket with Water

There was once a king of Persia who took delight in doing common things in uncommon ways.

At one time he was in need of a man who would always do just what he was told to do; and he took a very strange way to find him.

He sent out word that he wanted a man to work for him in his garden. More than a hundred came, and from among them he chose the two who seemed to be the brightest and quickest.

He showed them a large basket in the garden, and told them to fill it with water from a well.

After they had begun their work he left them, saying, "When the sun is down I will come and see your work.

If I find that you have done it well, I will pay you."

For a little while the two men carried water and poured it into the basket, without thinking much about it.

But at last one of them said, "What is the use of doing this foolish work? We can never fill the basket, for the water runs out of it as fast as we pour it in."

"That is none of our business," said the other man, whose name was Hassan. "The king has hired us to carry the water, and he must know why he wants it done. And then he has told us that if we do our work well, we shall be paid for it. What more could we want?"

"You may do as you please," said the first man. "But I am not going to work at anything so foolish, even for pay." And with that, he threw down his bucket and went away.

Hassan said not a word, but kept on carrying water all day long. At sunset the well was almost empty.

As he poured the last bucketful into the basket, he saw something in it that was very bright. He stooped and picked it up. It was a beautiful gold ring that his bucket had dipped up at the bottom of the well.

"Now I see the use of all this work," he said. "If the king had told me to empty the well, I should have poured

the water on the ground, and the ring would not have been found."

Just then the king came. As soon as he saw the ring, he knew that he had found the kind of man he wanted. He told Hassan to keep the ring for himself. "You have done so well in this one little thing," he said, "that now I know I can trust you with many things. You shall be the first of all my servants."

Do You Know?

1. What kind of man did the king of Persia need?
2. Why did the first man stop working?
3. Why did Hassan keep on working?
4. How was Hassan rewarded for his faithful work?

The Bible Says

"He that is faithful in that which is least is faithful also in much." —*Luke 16:10*

What People Do

A farmer grows food for us to eat.

A carpenter builds houses.

A nurse takes care of sick people.

A scientist studies God's world.

A doctor cures diseases.

A shepherd tends sheep.

A teacher helps people to learn.

An author writes books.

A pastor teaches people about God.

An artist makes beautiful pictures.

A missionary tells people about Jesus.

What will you do when you grow up?

What kinds of work do you do now?

Whatever you do, do it well.

The Bible Says

"Even a child is known by his doings, whether his work be pure, and whether it be right."
—*Proverbs 20:11*

Words to Watch For

Atri	dangers	fastened	justice
Italy	holidays	except	ashamed

Justice is fairness.

The Bell of Atri

Ding, dong, ding, dong, rang the bell of Atri.

Ding, dong, ding, dong, rang out the great bell again.

What did it mean?

People hurried to the market place to find out why the bell was ringing.

Atri was an old, old town in Italy. It was built on a hillside in the warm sunshine.

A very long time ago the king of Atri had a large bell hung in the market place. A long rope was fastened to the bell. The rope was so long that even little children could ring the great bell.

Then the king rode through the town and cried, "If anyone has been wronged let him ring the bell. Then the judge shall come to the square and there the wrongs shall be made right."

The old bell hung in the market place for years. Whenever anyone in Atri had been wronged, he rang the great bell and the judge made the wrongs right.

As the years went by, the rope wore out. It became so short that the tallest man in Atri could not reach it. So finally, one of the men in the town mended the rope with a piece of grape-vine which was long and strong.

On the hillside of Atri there lived a knight who had been a brave man. When he was young, he had fought in many battles. He had ridden through many strange lands. He liked to hunt in the forests, and he loved his dogs and horses.

As the knight grew older, he cared only for his money. He thought only of gold and how he might get more of it.

He sold everything that he had, everything except the horse which had carried him through so many dangers.

At last he said, "What is the use of keeping this lazy horse? He is eating his head off in my stable. Let him go and feed by the roadside. I want him only for the holidays."

So the faithful old horse was turned into the street. His only food was the dry grass that grew beside the road. No one cared for him, and no one gave him a kind word.

One warm summer afternoon the horse wandered into the market place. Near the open gate hung the grapevine which had just been fastened to the rope. The leaves on the grapevine were still fresh and green.

The half-starved horse took one mouthful and then another. With each bite the great bell of Atri rang out. It seemed to say, "Someone has done me a great wrong! Someone has done me a great wrong!"

The judge heard it. He put on his long robe and hurried to the market place.

No one was there, for the sun was very hot, but he saw the old horse eating away at the grapevine.

"Ah!" said the judge, "this horse belongs to the knight of Atri. He is ringing for justice. We all know how shamefully his master has treated him. Bring the knight here."

When the knight of Atri came into the market place, the judge said, "This horse has served you in his youth. He has saved you from many dangers. He has been faithful to you always. In return you shall care for him in his old age. You shall give him a green pasture in the summer and a warm stall in the winter."

The knight was ashamed and went quietly home.

The people shouted for joy as they led the old horse to his new stall.

When the good king of Atri heard it, he was glad and said, "My bell helps to right the wrongs of animals as well as those of men and women."

Words to Watch For

dancing   prancing   tying
elder   meantime   expect

The Sailor Man

Once upon a time, two children came to the house of a sailor man who lived beside the salt sea. They found the sailor man sitting in his doorway knotting ropes.

"How do you do?" asked the sailor man.

"We are very well, thank you," said the children, who had learned manners. "And we hope you are the same. We heard that you had a boat, and we thought that perhaps you would take us out in her and teach us how to sail."

"All in good time," said the sailor man. "I am busy now. But by and by, when my work is done, I may perhaps take one of you if you are ready to learn. Meantime here are some ropes that need knotting. You might be doing that, since it has to be done." He showed them how the knots should be tied, and went away and left them.

When he was gone, the first child ran to the window and looked out.

"There is the sea," he said. "The waves come up on the beach, almost to the door of the house. They run up all white, like prancing horses, and then they go dragging back. Come and look!"

"I cannot," said the second child. "I am tying a knot."

"Oh!" cried the first child, "I see the boat. She is dancing like a lady at a ball. I never saw such a beauty. Come and look!"

"I cannot," said the second child. "I am tying a knot."

"I shall have a delightful sail in that boat," said the first child. "I expect that the sailor man will take me, because I am the elder and I know more about it. There was no need of my watching when he showed you the knots, because I knew how already."

Just then the sailor man came in.

"Well," he said, "my work is over. What have you been doing in the meantime?"

"I have been looking at the boat," said the first child. "What a beauty she is! I shall have the best time in her that ever I had in my life."

"I have been tying knots," said the second child.

"Come, then," said the sailor man, and he held out his hand to the second child. "I will take you out in the boat and teach you to sail her."

"But I am the elder," cried the first child, "and I know a great deal more than she does."

"That may be," said the sailor man. "But a person must learn to tie a knot before he can learn to sail a boat."

"But I have learned to tie a knot," cried the child. "I know all about it!"

"How can I tell that?" asked the sailor man.

And he and the second child went off in the boat.

Do You Know Why?

1. Why did the two children go to see the sailor man?
2. Why did the sailor man say, "All in good time"?
3. Why did the sailor man want the children to learn to knot ropes?
4. Why did the second child not go to the window?
5. Why did the first child think that the sailor man would choose him for the boat ride?
6. Why did the first child think that he did not need to learn how to tie knots?
7. Why did the sailor man choose the second child rather than the first?

Ben Franklin
and the Ants

Words to Watch For

errands	noticed	office
sign	language	ceiling

Few people ever knew as many
things as Benjamin Franklin. Men
said, "How did he ever learn so much?"
For he had been a poor boy who had
to work for a living. He could not go
to school at all after he was ten years
old.

His father made soap and candles. Little Ben had to cut wicks for the candles. He also filled the candle molds, sold soap and candles, and ran errands. But when he was not at work, he spent his time reading good books.

He read the old story of <u>Pilgrim's Progress</u>, and liked it so well that he bought all the other stories by the same man.

Another way that he had of learning was by seeing things with his own eyes. His father took him to see carpenters at work with their saws and planes. He also saw masons laying bricks. He went to see men make the round legs of chairs.

Since Ben liked books so well, his father thought that it would be a good plan to send him to learn to print them. So the boy went to work in his brother's printing office. He worked hard, and whenever he had some time off he would read.

Long before he was a man, people said, "How much that Ben knows!" This was because—

He did not waste his time.
He read good books.
He worked hard at all his jobs.
He found out things for himself.

One thing that Ben wanted to find out about was how ants tell things to one another. He knew that they could not talk as we do, but he thought they must have a sign language. He noticed that when an ant has found a dead fly too big for him to drag away, he will run off and get some other ant to help him. Ben thought that ants must have some way of telling other ants that there is work to do.

One day he found some ants eating
molasses out of a little jar in a closet.
He shook them out. Then he tied a
string to the jar, and hung it on a nail
in the ceiling. One little ant liked
sweet things so well that he stayed
in the jar and kept on eating like a
greedy boy.

At last when this greedy ant had
eaten all that he could, he started to
go home. Ben saw him climb over the
rim of the jar. Then the ant ran down
the outside of the jar.

But when he got to the bottom, he
did not find any shelf there. He went
all around the jar. There was no way
to get down to the floor. The ant ran
this way and that way, but he could
not get down.

At last the greedy ant thought
he would see if he could go up. He

climbed up the string to the ceiling.
Then he went down the wall. At last
he came to his own hole.

After a while he got hungry again. He thought about that jar of sweets at the end of a string. Then he told the other ants.

In about half an hour after the ant had gone up the string, Ben saw some ants going down the string. They marched in a line, one after another. Soon there were two lines of ants on the string.

Then Ben Franklin knew that the greedy ant had told the other ants about the jar. He had not told them with his mouth. He had told them by making signs with his feelers.

If you watch ants the way Ben Franklin did, you can see them talking with their feelers, too. Do you know Who taught them to talk that way?

Phonics Word Lists

With Definitions and Practice Sentences

A. *To be read before introducing "Little Sunshine," p. 7.*

1. **wr** in **wr**inkle

write	wren	wrath	wrestle	wrinkle
wring	wrap	wrench	wrecker	wristband
wrong	wreath	wrist	wrapped	writing

2. Review of the suffixes -ed, -en, -ing, -er, -es, and -s

peeped	having	shining	walking	sparkled
opened	slowly	wiser	waiting	smiling
golden	coming	flying	branches	sounds

Dad can fix the pipe with a **wrench.**

Do you know what kind of bird a **wren** is?

3. Review of the prefixes a-, al-, and be-

almost	began	away	because
ago	around	always	belongs
across	another	already	behind

B. *To be read before introducing "The Raven and the Robin," p. 11.*

1. ould in could

could	would	should

2. c in city, ing in king, ong in long, old in gold, ea in thread, and ar in stars

place	songs	told	head	sharp
voice	long	colder	spread	marks
face	wings	folded	feathers	markings
decided	bring	sold	bread	starting

C. *To be read before introducing "Ring and the Bone," p. 17.*

1. **Contractions** *(A **contraction** is a quick way of saying two words at once. An apostrophe is used to show where letters have been left out.)*

I'll—I will	isn't—is not	he'll—he will
I'm—I am	didn't—did not	can't—can not
don't—do not	won't—will not	we're—we are
doesn't—does not	here's—here is	he's—he is
you're—you are	you'll—you will	we'll—we will

I hope it **doesn't** rain today.

Didn't we see that boy before?

He'll be here tomorrow.

2. **au** in f**au**cet, **ow** in b**ow**l, **dge** in fu**dge**, **ew** in fl**ew,** and **o** in sh**o**vel

Paul	follow	bridge	porridge	bottom
because	below	badges	knew	consider
saucer	owner	blew	renew	wonder
faulty	pillow	flew	autumn	money
cause	blowing	knew	smudge	ribbon

D. *To be read before introducing "Why the Deer Has Antlers," p. 23.*

1. **air** in h**air**

fair	flair	hairy	aircraft	airport
chair	repair	pair	airmail	unfair
stairs	fairly	dairy	airplane	fairness

Repair means to fix. My father will **repair** my bike.
If a thing is not fair, it is **unfair.**

2. **u** in p**u**sh

| bull | bushel | put | pushing | full |
| pull | putting | pulley | pulling | bushes |

3. **Review of long words**

animal	middle	understood	appetite
decided	quietly	antlers	afternoon
suppose	believed	wonderful	enter
discover	perfect	astronaut	maple

E. *To be read before introducing "Two Honest Men," p. 29.*

1. **ough** in en**ough, ou** in c**ou**ntry

rough	roughly	trouble	double	youngster
tough	enough	country	nervous	couple
roughen	young	cousin	generous	touch

2. **arr** in c**arr**y

carries	carrot	parrot	sparrow	Barry

3. **Review of compound words**

maybe	someone	anybody	anything
peanut	everyone	nobody	nothing
understand	together	everywhere	himself
something	sometime	roadside	everything
cupcake	pancake	herself	rainstorm

Mr. Andrew went on a **dangerous** journey.

A **sparrow** is a little bird.

F. *To be read before introducing "The Selfish Dog in the Manger," p. 33.*

1. **ire** in f**ire**

hire	spire	require	fireworks	desire
wire	admire	retire	inquire	tired

2. **ear** in b**ear, oo** in b**oo**k, **ew** in fl**ew**

tear	hook	chew	cooking	crooked
wear	woolly	flew	shook	blew

3. **Review of words with suffixes**

pant	snap	sadder	pull	hand
pants	snapping	sadly	pulls	handy
panted	snapper	saddest	pulling	handing

G. *To be read before introducing "The Way to Be Happy," p. 37.*

1. **Words in which the final *y* of the root word is changed to *i* before the addition of a suffix**

baby—babies	early—earlier	bunny—bunnies
tidy—tidier	happy—happier	shiny—shinier

2. Review of words with suffixes

smiled	trusted	crying	bothering	flying
owed	given	broken	sighing	booming
turned	ringing	sobbing	leader	fallen

H. *To be read before introducing "Lee and the Bird," p. 43.*

Review of long words and compound words

general	remain	suddenly	raindrops	battlefield
connect	distress	gigantic	cornstalk	suppose
without	foolish	someone	impossible	applesauce

I. *To be read before introducing "Eyvind's Goat," p. 47.*

1. Review of words with suffixes and prefixes

calling	broken	unhappy	beginning	waked
beside	stretched	opened	dreaming	started
tasted	belongs	plowing	gathered	ripened

2. air in h**air, ie** in browni**e, old** in g**old, ould** in c**ould,** and **ou** in c**ou**ntry

chair	piece	hold	would	couple
stairway	field	sold	should	touch
fairness	belief	folder	couldn't	young

J. *To be read before introducing "The Rain-drops," p. 55.*

a in ban**a**n**a**

central	America	buffalo	purchase	package
distant	abundant	thousands	several	valuable

K. *To be read before introducing "The First Thanksgiving," p. 59.*

1. -ful in beauti**ful, -est** in bigg**est**

faithful	cupful	cheerful	loudest	largest
mouthful	useful	thankful	kindest	biggest

Jim is full of thanks. He is **thankful.**

This is a full cup of flour. It is a **cupful.**

Ted is big. Jeff is bigger. Todd is the **biggest** of all.

2. **are** in **care**

dare	mare	scare	careless	aware
hare	rare	square	compare	beware
careful	glare	share	spare	declare

L. *To be read before introducing "The Milk-maid," p. 67.*

tain in moun**tain**

mountain	certain	fountain	captain
curtain	certainly	mountainous	curtains

M. *To be read before introducing "The Frog and the Ox," p. 69.*

Review of words in which *y* is changed to *i* before the addition of a suffix.

sleepy	heavy	tidy	lonely	easy
sleepier	heavily	tidier	loneliest	easier
sleepiest	heavier	tidiest	lonelier	easily

N. *To be read before introducing "The Boy Who Cried Wolf," p. 73.*

1. **ure** in p**ure**

cure   surely   purely   secure   enduring

2. **ture** in pas**ture**

capture   lecture   future   rapture   moisture

culture   nature   picture   furniture   adventure

A **pasture** is a field.

Capture means to catch.

O. *To be read before introducing "David, the Shepherd Boy," p. 77.*

1. **war** in **war**m

warm   warn   reward   award   warning

2. **Review of words that can be divided between two vowels**

lion   trial   cruel   science   diet

giant   dial   poet   Samuel   quiet

P. *To be read before introducing "All about Crabs," p. 85.*

1. **tion** in na**tion**

station	action	attention	foundation	adoption
motion	fraction	decoration	invitation	protection

2. **eigh** in **eigh**t

neigh	weigh	freight	eighteen	weightless
sleigh	weight	eighty	neighbor	freighter

Q. *To be read before introducing "Filling a Basket with Water," p. 91.*

tain in moun**tain**, **ture** in pas**ture**, **tion** in na**tion**, **eigh** in **eigh**t, **ful** in beauti**ful**

fountain	capture	eighty	invention	truthful
captain	nature	freight	creation	harmful

A **faithful** person is one who keeps on
doing what is right.

R. *To be read before introducing "What People Do," p. 95.*

or in sail**or, ar** in doll**ar**

cedar	tailor	beggar	collector	operation
popular	actor	collar	conductor	pastor
caterpillar	color	cellar	elevator	doctor

Everybody likes Carol. She is a **popular** girl.

What **flavor** is this ice-cream cone?

Strong and True
Guide to Story Themes